The

GREAT BRITISH
QUIZ BOOK

The

GREAT BRITISH
QUIZ BOOK

Published in paperback in 2012.
Printed by Clays Limited

A Mirror publication
Head of Syndication & Licensing: Fergus McKenna.
Daily Mirror: David Scripps.
020 7293 3858

Trinity Mirror Media

Produced by Trinity Mirror Media,
PO Box 48, Liverpool L69 3EB
0151 227 2000

Executive Editor: Ken Rogers.
Senior Editor: Steve Hanrahan.
Senior Art Editor: Rick Cooke.
Senior Editor: Paul Dove.
Production: Adam Oldfield.
Cover Design: Matthew Barnes.

ISBN: 978-1-907324-22-2

Mirror

Wills & Kate

GREAT
BRITISH

God save our gracious Queen! Long live our noble Queen!

ROYALS ▶▶▶

Charles & Camilla

Part 1

JUBILEE AND THE QUEEN

Q1. The Queen celebrated her Diamond Jubilee, but in which year was she formally crowned Queen?

....

Q2. Which sporting event did the Queen attend during the Diamond Jubilee weekend festivities?

....

Q3. What was the name of the Royal Barge that sailed down the Thames?

....

PART 1: JUBILEE AND THE QUEEN

Q4. A BBC concert took place on Monday, 4th June, 2012 featuring many pop stars. What was the location for this event?

....

Q5. A network of how many beacons was lit across the country to commemorate the Jubilee Weekend?

....

Q6. A procession and service were held on day four of the Jubilee celebrations. Where was the service held?

....

PART 1: JUBILEE AND THE QUEEN

Q7. What is the date of the Queen's actual birthday?

....

Q8. What is the date of the Queen's official birthday?

....

Q9. In what year was the Queen born?

....

Q10. Who is the only other British monarch to have celebrated a Diamond Jubilee?

....

PART 1: JUBILEE AND THE QUEEN

Q11. Where was the Queen born?

....

Q12. What are the Queen's other two Christian names?

....

Q13. The Queen spent much of her childhood living in Royal Lodge. In which park was the lodge situated?

....

Q14. Up to an including 2012, how many Prime Ministers have served under the Queen?

....

PART 1: JUBILEE AND THE QUEEN

Q15. Who was the first Prime Minister to serve under the Queen?

....

Q16. How many Popes have visited the UK during the Queen's reign?

....

Q17. The Queen was the first British monarch to use which mode of transport?

....

PART 1: JUBILEE AND THE QUEEN

Q18. Where is the Queen's official residence in Scotland?

....

Q19. What Royal 'first' was launched by the Queen in 1997?

....

Q20. In which year did the Queen marry the Duke of Edinburgh?

....

Part 2
WILLS & KATE

Q1. In what year was Prince William born?

....

Q2. What is the Duchess of Cambridge's maiden name?

....

Q3. Where did William and Kate get married?

....

▶▶▶

PART 2: WILLS & KATE

Q4. On what date did the Royal couple tie the knot?

....

Q5. What was Kate's job before she married William?

....

Q6. For whom did Kate work prior to marrying William?

....

Q7. What are the names of Kate's two siblings?

....

PART 2: WILLS & KATE

Q8. In 2007, William was promoted to the rank of Lieutenant in which regiment?

....

Q9. What was William's rank in the Royal Air Force when he graduated from his training in September, 2010?

....

Q10. What other two titles were bestowed upon William when he was given the title Duke of Cambridge by the Queen?

....

Q11. Where was William sent on a six-week operational deployment in February, 2012?

....

Q12. Which sport did Kate play for St. Andrews University whilst studying there?

....

Q13. Which college did Kate attend prior to embarking on her gap year and eventually enrolling as a student at St. Andrews University in 2001?

....

PART 2: WILLS & KATE

Q14. In which Berkshire town was Kate born?

....

Q15. During William's gap year, in which Central American country did he spend time preparing for survival exercises with the Welsh Guards?

....

Q16. Where was Prince William born?

....

Q17. How has Prince William been known in the military since completion of his training in 2010?

....

PART 2: WILLS & KATE

Q18. What are the names of Kate's parents?

....

Q19. Kate formerly worked as a part-time buyer for which children's clothing company?

....

Q20. Which part of the world did William and Kate visit in 2012 as part of the Queen's Jubilee celebrations?

....

Part 3

CHARLES & CAMILLA

Q1. What is the maiden name of the Duchess of Cornwall?

....

Q2. What are Prince Charles's other three Christian names?

....

Q3. In which location did the investiture of the Prince of Wales take place in 1969?

....

▶▶▶

PART 3: CHARLES & CAMILLA

Q4. What rank in the Royal Air Force is held by Prince Charles?

....

Q5. What is the name of Charles and Camilla's private residence in Scotland?

....

Q6. What honour was bestowed upon Camilla by the Queen in April, 2012?

....

Q7. Charles spent two terms in 1966 as an exchange student at which remote school in Australia?

....

PART 3: CHARLES & CAMILLA

Q8. Where did Charles and Camilla marry on 9th April, 2005?

....

Q9. How old was Charles when the Queen made him Prince of Wales?

....

Q10. Which preparatory school in Berkshire did Charles attend from 1957 to 1962?

....

Q11. What is Camilla's middle name?

....

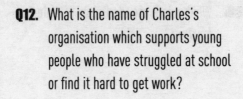

PART 3: CHARLES & CAMILLA

Q12. What is the name of Charles's organisation which supports young people who have struggled at school or find it hard to get work?

....

Q13. Which other title does Charles use when undertaking royal duties in Scotland?

....

Q14. What is the motto of the Prince of Wales?

....

PART 3: CHARLES & CAMILLA

Q15. What colour are the Prince of Wales's feathers?

....

Q16. What competition for schools was created by the Duchess of Cornwall as part of the Queen's Diamond Jubilee celebrations?

....

Q17. Who was the last person to hold the title Prince of Wales before Charles?

....

PART 3: CHARLES & CAMILLA

Q18. Where was Charles born on 14th November, 1948?

....

Q19. Which Cambridge University college did Charles attend?

....

Q20. What title does Charles hold in the Royal Navy?

....

Part 4

REST OF
THE ROYALS

Q1. What title did the Queen bestow upon
Prince Edward on his marriage in 1999?

....

Q2. By what royal title is Sophie
Rhys-Jones now known?

....

Q3. What hereditary title was bestowed
upon Prince Andrew on his marriage
in 1986?

....

►►►

PART 4: REST OF THE ROYALS

Q4. What other two royal titles were bestowed upon Prince Andrew in 1986?

....

Q5. What title did the Queen bestow upon Princess Anne in 1987?

....

Q6. Where is Princess Anne's home?

....

Q7. What relation is Prince Michael to the Queen?

....

PART 4: REST OF THE ROYALS

Q8. What was the Duchess of Kent's maiden name prior to marrying the Duke of Kent?

....

Q9. The Duke and Duchess of Gloucester reside in which London palace?

....

Q10. If any of the Queen's children were required to use a surname, what would it be?

....

PART 4: REST OF THE ROYALS

Q11. As at 2012, who is the highest-ranking female in line to the throne?

Q12. What was the name of Prince Edward's theatrical production company which he ran for nearly 10 years?

Q13. Which TV award did Princess Anne win in 1971?

PART 4: REST OF THE ROYALS

Q14. Who did Princess Alexandra marry in 1963?

....

Q15. Where were Prince Andrew and Sarah Ferguson married in 1986?

....

Q16. Baroness Marie-Christine von Reibnitz married into the Royal Family in 1978. What is her royal title?

....

Q17. When was Prince Harry born?

....

PART 4: REST OF THE ROYALS

Q18. Which school did Harry attend when he sat his GCSE's and A Levels?

....

Q19. What are Harry's two favourite sports?

....

Q20. Harry made an ITV documentary about victims of AIDS whilst in which African country during his gap year?

....

PART 4: REST OF THE ROYALS

Q21. What are Harry's Christian names?

....

Q22. What rank was Harry promoted to in the Blues and Royals in April, 2011?

....

Q23. Harry is related to which emperor through his paternal grandfather?

....

▶▶▶

PART 4: REST OF THE ROYALS

Q24. Harry's long-term on-off relationship with which girl finally ended in 2010?

....

Q25. Where is Harry's principal London residence?

....

Q26. Harry is now a fully operational pilot of which military aircraft?

....

PART 4: REST OF THE ROYALS

Q27. On which Greek island was Prince Philip born?

....

Q28. What relation was Prince Philip to Earl Mountbatten of Burma?

....

Q29. In which year was Prince Philip born?

....

Q30. Who is the great-great grandmother of both Prince Philip and the Queen?

....

PART 4: REST OF THE ROYALS

Q31. What rank did Prince Philip rise to until his naval career ended in 1951?

....

Q32. What pilot scheme for boys did Prince Philip launch in 1956?

....

Q33. What television 'first' did Prince Philip achieve in 1961?

....

Q34. As well as being Duke of Edinburgh, what other two royal titles does Prince Philip hold?

....

PART 4: REST OF THE ROYALS

Q35. How many siblings did Prince Philip have?

....

Q36. Which British school did Prince Philip attend, the same school that has since been attended by his three sons?

....

Q37. Who married Peter Phillips in St George's Chapel, Windsor Castle in 2008?

....

PART 4: REST OF THE ROYALS

Q38. What royal title is held by Princess Margaret's son, David Armstrong-Jones?

....

Q39. The Earl of Ulster is the son of which Duke?

....

Q40. What is the name of the former Scottish holiday home of the Queen Mother?

....

Part 5

PAST BRITISH MONARCHS

Q1. Who became the first monarch of the United Kingdom in 1603?

....

Q2. What name is given to the period between 1649 and 1660 when there was no monarch of the United Kingdom?

....

Q3. Who was the last monarch of the House of Stuart?

....

PART 5: PAST BRITISH MONARCHS

Q4. Who was the longest-reigning British king, having reigned from 1760-1820?

....

Q5. Who was the monarch immediately before Queen Victoria came to the throne?

....

Q6. In which year did Victoria become Queen of the United Kingdom?

....

PART 5: PAST BRITISH MONARCHS

Q7. Who was the only British monarch of the House of Saxe-Coburg-Gotha?

....

Q8. Which monarch was the first to make a Christmas broadcast to the nation?

....

Q9. What royal title was bestowed upon Edward VIII following his abdication in 1936?

....

PART 5: PAST BRITISH MONARCHS

Q10. How did Lady Elizabeth Bowes-Lyon become known to the nation in her later life?

....

Q11. Which king restored the monarchy in 1660 after a period of eleven years?

....

Q12. Who invaded England in 1688 and removed James II from the throne?

....

PART 5: PAST BRITISH MONARCHS

Q13. What did the Act of Settlement of 1701 prohibit by law?

....

Q14. Caroline of Brunswick was the Consort of which British monarch?

....

Q15. What nationality was Alexandra, wife of Edward VII?

....

Q16. Who was the first monarch of the House of Hanover, who ruled from 1714 to 1727?

....

PART 5: PAST BRITISH MONARCHS

Q17. Mary of Teck was Queen Consort to which monarch?

....

Q18. Which English king was nicknamed 'The Lionheart'?

....

Q19. Who was the last of Henry VIII's wives, the only one to outlive him?

....

Q20. Charles III, also known as The Young Pretender, is best remembered in history by what name?

....

GREAT
BRITISH

Jessica Ennis ... Ellie Simmonds ... Andy Murray ...

SPORT ▶▶▶

Olympic & Paralympic Games

Part 1

2012 OLYMPICS

Q1. How many medals did Team GB win at the 2012 Olympics?

....

Q2. How many gold medals did Team GB win?

....

Q3. Which British athlete just missed out on a medal in the men's 400 metres hurdles final, finishing fourth?

....

▶▶▶

PART 1: 2012 OLYMPICS

Q4. Which British athlete won gold in the 5,000 and 10,000 metres finals?

....

Q5. Which British athlete quietly went about his task to win the men's long jump gold medal?

....

Q6. In which two events in the pool did Britain's Rebecca Adlington win bronze medals?

....

Q7. Who won gold for Britain in the men's cycling sprint?

....

PART 1: 2012 OLYMPICS

Q8. Who cycled to gold in the men's keirin event?

....

Q9. Which Briton won a bronze medal in the men's cycling omnium?

....

Q10. Victoria Pendleton won gold in which women's cycling event?

....

Q11. Who was Britain's gold medal-winning heroine in the women's cycling omnium?

....

Q12. Who was Heather Stanning's rowing partner in Britain's women's pair gold medal-winning duo?

....

Q13. Katherine Grainger and Anna Watkins won gold for Britain in which event?

....

Q14. Who did Andy Murray beat to win the Olympic tennis men's singles gold medal?

....

PART 1: 2012 OLYMPICS

Q15. Who did Andy Murray partner to win the Olympic mixed doubles silver medal?

....

Q16. Who were the brothers who won gold and bronze medals in the men's triathlon?

....

Q17. Which British boxer won the women's gold medal in the flyweight division?

....

PART 1: 2012 OLYMPICS

Q18. At what boxing weight did Anthony Joshua win a gold medal for Britain?

....

Q19. On which piece of gymnastics apparatus did Louis Smith and Max Whitlock collect silver and bronze medals respectively?

....

Q20. Which British gymnast won a bronze medal for her performance on the uneven bars?

....

PART 1: 2012 OLYMPICS

Q21. From this list of Olympic venues,
name the events that were held there:

a. Box Hill

....

b. City of Coventry Stadium

....

c. Earls Court

....

d. Eton Dornay

....

e. Greenwich Park

....

Part 2

2012
PARALYMPICS

Q1. In what position did Great Britain finish in the medals table?

....

Q2. How many medals did Great Britain win at the Games?

....

Q3. How many of these were gold medals?

....

▶▶▶

PART 2: 2012 PARALYMPICS

Q4. Who won four cycling gold medals for Great Britain in women's road and track events?

....

Q5. Who won gold medals for Great Britain in four athletics T54 events?

....

Q6. In which sport did Sophie Christiansen win three gold medals for Great Britain?

....

Q7. Swimmer Eleanor Simmonds won four medals for Great Britain. In which two events did she win gold?

....

Q8. Which Briton won two equestrian gold medals on her horse Cabral?

....

Q9. Which Briton won athletic gold medals in the women's 100m and 200m T34 events?

....

PART 2: 2012 PARALYMPICS

Q10. In which sport did Britain's Heather Frederiksen win four medals, including one gold?

....

Q11. In which sport did Mark Colbourne win one gold and two silver medals?

....

Q12. 17-year old Oliver Hynd won three swimming medals, but in which event did he win his only gold medal?

....

PART 2: 2012 PARALYMPICS

Q13. In which sport did Danielle Brown and Mel Clarke win gold and silver for Britain?

....

Q14. Britain won 29 medals in the athletics events. How many of these were gold medals?

....

Q15. Who won gold for Britain in the men's 100m T44 race in a new Paralympics record time of 10.90 seconds?

....

PART 2: 2012 PARALYMPICS

Q16. Samuel Ingram won a silver medal for Britain in which contact sport?

....

Q17. Who won a bronze medal for Britain in the women's 40kg powerlifting event?

....

Q18. A British team won gold in which rowing event?

....

Q19. How many swimming medals did Britain win in total?

....

PART 2: 2012 PARALYMPICS

Q20. Great Britain won medals in which two wheelchair tennis events?

....

Q21. How many swimming gold medals did British swimmers win?

....

Q22. Which British swimmer won gold in the women's 200m freestyle S14 race?

....

▶▶▶

PART 2: 2012 PARALYMPICS

Q23. Swimmer Jonathan Fox won gold for Britain in which event?

....

Q24. Helena Lucas won Britain's only gold medal in which sport?

....

Q25. In which throwing event did Aled Davies win gold for Britain?

....

Part 3

GREAT BRITISH SPORTING EVENTS

The first 10 questions here are about tennis, to mark Andy Murray's remarkable year and the breakthrough of Laura Robson in the women's game...

Q1. Who defeated Andy Murray in the final of Wimbledon 2012?

....

Q2. Who won the Wimbledon ladies' singles crown for the fifth time in 2012?

....

▶▶▶

PART 3: BRITISH SPORTING EVENTS

Q3. Which British player became the first Briton to win the men's doubles title for 76 years when he partnered Freddie Nielsen to victory in 2012?

....

Q4. Who defeated Laura Robson in the 4th round of the 2012 US Open to end her great run in the tournament?

....

Q5. Who became the British number one ladies player in July, 2012?

....

PART 3: BRITISH SPORTING EVENTS

Q6. Britain had four ladies in or around the world top 100 rankings in 2012. Laura Robson, Heather Watson and which other two players?

....

Q7. Who beat Andy Murray in five sets in the semi-finals of the Australian Open in 2012?

....

Q8. Who did Andy Murray defeat to win the 2012 US Open and win his first Grand Slam title?

....

PART 3: BRITISH SPORTING EVENTS

Q9. Which Spaniard knocked Andy Murray out at the quarter final stage of the 2012 French Open?

....

Q10. Who is the British men's number two who lost in the second round of Wimbledon in 2012?

....

Q11. In which year was the Grand National first officially run?

....

PART 3: BRITISH SPORTING EVENTS

Q12. Which race, first staged in 1829, is traditionally held on the last Saturday of March or the first Saturday of April every year?

....

Q13. Diomed was the first winner of which race in 1780?

....

Q14. As at 2012, which cricket side has won most English County Cricket championships?

....

PART 3: BRITISH SPORTING EVENTS

Q15. How many Scottish golf courses are venues for the Open Championship (as at 2012)?

....

Q16. Which event is held on the River Thames in Oxfordshire for five days every year in July?

....

Q17. Entry Badge was the first winner of which race, originally held at White City but since 1985 at Wimbledon?

....

PART 3: BRITISH SPORTING EVENTS

Q18. Where in Britain is the world's largest sailing regatta held every year for a week?

....

Q19. After Wembley Stadium, what is Britain's largest stadium by capacity?

....

Q20. Which four venues have hosted the formula one British Grand Prix since its inception in 1926?

....

Part 4

FOOTBALL AND EURO 2012

These questions are all about winners and losers in football during 2012...

Q1. Which team reached the final of both the FA Cup and League Cup?

....

Q2. Which Championship side lost in the final of the League Cup, losing on penalties?

....

▶▶▶

PART 4: FOOTBALL

Q3. Which three teams won promotion from the Championship to the Premier League?

....

Q4. Who replaced Nick Barmby as manager of Hull City in June?

....

Q5. Everton signed striker Nikica Jelavic in January for £5.5m, from which club?

....

Q6. Who was the Premier League's top scorer for season 2011/12 with 30 goals?

....

▶▶▶

PART 4: FOOTBALL

Q7. Which Englishman received the Premier League Manager of the Season award?

....

Q8. Which three teams were relegated from the Premier League?

....

Q9. Which team replaced Rangers in the Scottish Premier League following Rangers' demotion to the SFL Third Division?

....

PART 4: FOOTBALL

Q10. Which team won the Barclays Premier League fair play award in 2012 for having fewest yellow and red cards?

....

Q11. Which three teams were relegated from the Championship to the First Division?

....

Q12. Which Southampton striker was the Championship's top scorer for 2011/12 with 27 goals?

....

PART 4: FOOTBALL

Q13. Which Championship side went into administration in February for the second time in three years?

....

Q14. Who were the three unsuccessful clubs that contested the play-offs from the Championship?

....

Q15. Which team was relegated from the Scottish Premier League?

....

Q16. Which team won the First Division title with 101 points, eight points more than the team that finished second?

....

PART 4: FOOTBALL

Q17. Which four teams contested the First Division play-offs?

....

Q18. Which team won the First Division play-offs final?

....

Q19. Huddersfield Town's Scottish striker was the First Division's top scorer for 2011/12 with 36 goals. Who is he?

....

Q20. Name any two of the four clubs relegated from the First Division at the end of season 2011/12.

....

PART 4: EURO 2012

Q1. Which two countries hosted the Euro 2012 finals?

....

Q2. Spain won Euro 2012, but which team did they defeat 4-0 in the final?

....

Q3. France, Sweden and which other country made up England's group?

....

PART 4: EURO 2012

Q4. Who scored England's goal in their opening 1-1 draw with France?

....

Q5. Which team finished second in England's group?

....

Q6. How many points did England amass when winning their group?

....

PART 4: EURO 2012

Q7. Who were the two losing semi-finalists?

....

Q8. How many teams contested the Euro 2012 finals?

....

Q9. In which city was the final of Euro 2012 held?

....

Q10. Which Irish player received a red card in the match against Italy?

....

Part 5

GENERAL SPORT IN 2012

Q1. Which horse stretched its winning run to 14 out of 14 races when it triumphed at Ascot in October and was then retired to stud?

....

Q2. Which Aiden O'Brien trained horse won the Epsom Derby by five lengths?

....

Q3. Which horse won the Grand National in a photo finish with Sunnyhillboy?

....

▶▶▶

PART 5: GENERAL SPORT IN 2012

Q4. Why was the name of the winner of the Oaks at Epsom in June unusual?

....

Q5. Who won the 2011/12 British Jump Jockeys Championship in April?

....

Q6. Which country won the 2012 Six Nations championship?

....

Q7. Which team picked up the wooden spoon in the Six Nations championship, having lost all five matches?

....

▶▶▶

PART 5: GENERAL SPORT IN 2012

Q8. What was the final score in the 2012 Ryder Cup when Europe beat the USA team to retain the trophy?

....

Q9. Which club won the 2012 Aviva Premiership final by a score of 30-23?

....

Q10. Which two teams contested the final of the 2012 Rugby League Challenge Cup?

....

Q11. Who won the 2012 British Open in July giving him his fourth golfing ´major´?

....

PART 5: GENERAL SPORT IN 2012

Q12. Who claimed his second golfing 'major' when he won the US PGA title in August?

....

Q13. Which American won his first golfing 'major' when he triumphed in the US Masters at Augusta in April?

....

Q14. Which American golfer was a surprise winner of the 2012 US Open at the Olympic Club, San Francisco?

....

PART 5: GENERAL SPORT IN 2012

Q15. Over which course was the 2012 British Open golf championship played?

....

Q16. For which Formula One team did Fernando Alonso drive in 2012?

....

Q17. Who won his first-ever Formula One Grand Prix when he triumphed in the Spanish Grand Prix in May, 2012?

....

PART 5: GENERAL SPORT IN 2012

Q18. Driving for Red Bull Racing-Renault, who captured the British Grand Prix in July, 2012?

....

Q19. Which team had back-to-back victories in the Hungarian and Belgium Grand Prix races in 2012?

....

Q20. Vitaly Petrov was the only driver from which country in the 2012 Formula One season?

....

Q21. Who won the 2012 PDC World Darts Championship, beating Andy Hamilton in the final?

....

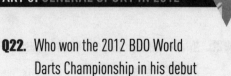

PART 5: GENERAL SPORT IN 2012

Q22. Who won the 2012 BDO World Darts Championship in his debut appearance in the tournament?

....

Q23. Who won his fourth Snooker World Championship when he defeated Ali Carter 18-11 in the final?

....

Q24. Which team won Superbowl XLVI in February, defeating New England Patriots 21-17?

....

PART 5: GENERAL SPORT IN 2012

Q25. Who knocked out Amir Khan in Las Vegas in July in a World Light-Welterweight title fight?

....

Q26. Who won the 2012 Tour de France, becoming the first British cyclist to do so?

....

Q27. Who announced in August that he would retire from professional cricket with immediate effect?

....

PART 5: GENERAL SPORT IN 2012

Q28. What was the result of the three-match Test series between England and West Indies?

....

Q29. Which side won the 2012 First Division County Championship?

....

Q30. Which British cyclist won a record 23 stage wins in the Tour de France when he triumphed in the last stage of the 2012 race?

....

British Politics

GREAT BRITISH

HEADLINE

Leveson Inquiry .... Coalition .... Double-dip Recession

MAKERS ▶▶▶

Part 1

BRITISH POLITICS

Q1. What did the Scottish Parliament announce would be held in the autumn of 2014?

....

Q2. In 2012, which Cabinet minister resigned over allegations that his wife took speeding points on her licence on his behalf?

....

PART 1: BRITISH POLITICS

Q3. Why did Falkirk MP Eric Joyce make news headlines in February, 2012?

....

Q4. Which controversial political figure won the Bradford West by-election in March with a majority of over 10,000?

....

Q5. Which Cabinet minister reportedly said "I have declared war on Mr Murdoch and I think we are going to win", referring to News Corporation's bid for BSKYB?

....

PART 1: BRITISH POLITICS

Q6. In 2009, which national newspaper published revelations about MPs' expenses claims?

....

Q7. Which former leader of the Conservative Party did David Cameron appoint as Foreign Secretary in 2010?

....

Q8. Which Oxfordshire constituency has David Cameron as its MP?

....

PART 1: BRITISH POLITICS

Q9. Who was the First Minister of Northern Ireland who stood down for six weeks in 2010 following revelations about his wife's personal life?

....

Q10. Who was the Chief Secretary to the Treasury who resigned in May, 2010 over newspaper allegations of expenses claimed for paying rent to his boyfriend?

....

Q11. Who was the Defence Secretary forced to resign in October, 2011 over revelations about his friendship with businessman Adam Werrity?

....

PART 1: BRITISH POLITICS

Q12. Who was David Cameron's former Communications Director subsequently charged by police over phone hacking allegations?

....

Q13. Who did Gordon Brown surprisingly bring back into the Labour Cabinet in 2008?

....

Q14. Why did Nick Clegg make a public, abject apology in September, 2012 for something he did two years earlier?

....

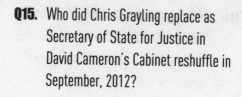

PART 1: BRITISH POLITICS

Q15. Who did Chris Grayling replace as Secretary of State for Justice in David Cameron's Cabinet reshuffle in September, 2012?

....

Q16. Who was the Culture Secretary accused of having improper contact with News Corporation at the time of their takeover bid for BSkyB?

....

Q17. Who became Britain's third-youngest Foreign Secretary when Gordon Brown appointed him to the post in 2007?

....

PART 1: BRITISH POLITICS

Q18. Why did newly-appointed Chief Whip Andrew Mitchell rant at police in Downing Street in September, 2012?

....

Q19. Who was elected leader of the UK Independence Party (UKIP) for the second time in November, 2010?

....

Q20. As at September, 2012, how many Scottish Nationalist Party MPs were in Westminster?

....

Part 2

NEWS STORIES AT HOME AND ABROAD

All of these events took place in 2012, some at home and others further afield. The first 20 questions relate to events at home...

Q1. Who chaired the inquiry into alleged phone hacking by newspaper journalists?

....

Q2. Who is the former Chief Executive of News International who was charged in connection with phone hacking allegations?

....

▶▶▶

PART 2: NEWS STORIES – HOME

Q3. Which father and son gave evidence to the phone hacking inquiry?

....

Q4. Why did Gary Dobson and David Norris make headlines when jailed for an offence they committed 19 years previously?

....

Q5. Who is the former CEO of the Royal Bank of Scotland stripped of his knighthood as a result of the near collapse of the bank in 2008?

....

PART 2: NEWS STORIES – HOME

Q6. The first edition of which new tabloid newspaper appeared on 26th February, 2012?

....

Q7. Which three British cities were granted city status to mark the Queen's Diamond Jubilee?

....

Q8. Which religious figure announced his intention to retire from his post at the end of 2012?

....

PART 2: NEWS STORIES – HOME

Q9. The cost of first and second class stamps rose in April, 2012. What were the new rates?

....

Q10. The 100th anniversary of which tragic event was commemorated around the world on 15th April, 2012?

....

Q11. What arrived in Cornwall from Athens on 18th May, 2012?

....

PART 2: NEWS STORIES – HOME

Q12. Why did Royal Navy Lieutenant Commander Sarah West make history?

....

Q13. Which bank was fined £290 million for trying to manipulate inter-bank interest rates?

....

Q14. Who took over as the next Director-General of the BBC in the autumn of 2012?

....

PART 2: NEWS STORIES – HOME

Q15. Which new London landmark was officially opened on 5th July, 2012?

....

Q16. Virgin Trains controversially lost the West Coast rail franchise to which bidder, only for the decision to be put on hold pending an investigation?

....

Q17. Which former tycoon was found guilty of stealing millions of pounds from his company?

....

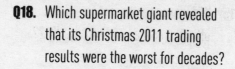

PART 2: NEWS STORIES – HOME

Q18. Which supermarket giant revealed that its Christmas 2011 trading results were the worst for decades?

....

Q19. Which country granted Julian Assange political asylum and allowed him to stay in its London embassy?

....

Q20. Why was the date 6th February, 2012 a special date for the United Kingdom?

....

PART 2: NEWS STORIES – ABROAD

Q1. China introduced a ban to stop people keeping what from being more than 20 inches tall?

....

Q2. Who did Mitt Romney welcome to the US election race as his Vice Presidential running mate?

....

Q3. Which popular holiday islands were ravaged by wildfires?

....

PART 2: NEWS STORIES – ABROAD

Q4. Which bank was accused by the US of secretly channelling money destined for Iranian clients?

....

Q5. Why were the three members of the Russian female punk band Pussy Riot jailed?

....

Q6. What sporting event was hosted jointly by Poland and Ukraine in June?

....

PART 2: NEWS STORIES – ABROAD

Q7. Why did 'Curiosity' make headline news?

....

Q8. The Abraj al-Bait Towers were completed in 2012, making this the second-tallest building in the world. Where is it located?

....

Q9. 73 people died in a fight between rival fans at which sporting event?

....

PART 2: NEWS STORIES – ABROAD

Q10. In which European city did 80,000 people protest in February, 2012 over austerity measures being proposed due to the economic crisis?

....

Q11. A plot to assassinate which world leader was uncovered by intelligence forces?

....

Q12. Why was American Staff Sergeant Robert Bales in the news in March?

....

PART 2: NEWS STORIES – ABROAD

Q13. What was the name of the cruise ship that capsized off the island of Giglio, having struck a rock?

....

Q14. Who became President of France following the French general elections in May?

....

Q15. Which former dictator was jailed for life for being an accomplice in the killing of unarmed protestors in his own country?

....

PART 2: NEWS STORIES – ABROAD

Q16. Which country suffered a massive power failure leading to more than half of the population being without electricity?

....

Q17. What was the name of the hurricane that caused devastation along the Gulf Coast of America in August, 2012?

....

Q18. Which country held its first national elections since ousting its former dictator leader?

....

PART 2: NEWS STORIES – ABROAD

Q19. Which European country was hit by a magnitude 6.0 earthquake in May, 2012?

....

Q20. A woman in Virginia, USA bought a painting in a flea market for $50, now thought to be by which famous artist and worth up to $100,000?

....

Part 3

ODD AND FUNNY STORIES

Some amusing news stories from home and abroad.

Q1. A fleet of Ferraris set a new world record for the biggest-ever supercar parade. How many cars lined up at Silverstone?

....

Q2. Who has been banned by North Devon District Council from collecting money for charity over a permit row?

....

PART 3: ODD & FUNNY STORIES

Q3. Zeus was declared to be the world's tallest what, standing at 44 inches tall?

....

Q4. Walter Samaszko died leaving only $200 in his bank account, but what did police find when they entered his home in Carson City, Nevada?

....

Q5. What returned for cook June Blythe after 40 years?

....

PART 3: ODD & FUNNY STORIES

Q6. What accolade did commuters bestow upon a car park in Castle Street, Leeds?

....

Q7. What was unusual about Northampton Borough Council's letter inviting Oakley Barrett to a housing strategy meeting?

....

Q8. Who could receive a state funeral if the bones found under a Leicester car park prove to be his?

....

PART 3: ODD & FUNNY STORIES

Q9. What has New York City banned in an effort to combat obesity?

....

Q10. The Astronomer Royal has said what about people who claim to have seen UFOs?

....

Q11. What plea did death row prisoner Ronald Post make to a court?

....

PART 3: ODD & FUNNY STORIES

Q12. A French man had to have his right hand amputated after he was accidentally shot. Who shot him?

....

Q13. What did smugglers swallow in an attempt to smuggle it into Colombia?

....

Q14. A Scottish chip shop owner has been warned to withdraw his application for special status for which food 'delicacy'?

....

PART 3: ODD & FUNNY STORIES

Q15. Why were medical staff at Camp Bastion in Afghanistan caught by surprise in September, 2012?

....

Q16. A singing version of which politician's apology turned out to be an internet hit?

....

Q17. According to research, people who follow which pastime earn more at work than people who don't?

....

PART 3: ODD & FUNNY STORIES

Q18. 78-year old Peter Glazebrook set a world record for growing the world's biggest what, weighing in at 18lbs 1oz?

....

Q19. What appropriate action did bird fancier Bill Oddie take to help people understand bird sounds?

....

Q20. The New Guinness World Records Book was published in 2012. Which edition of the book was this?

....

Part 4

THE GOOD AND THE BAD OF BRITAIN

There have been some great Brits, some good Brits and some not so good. We begin with ten questions on the good...

Q1. Who is the legendary hero who supported Richard the Lionheart and robbed from the rich to give to the poor?

....

Q2. He was good, at least from a Scottish point of view, for his legendary battles against the English. Who was he?

....

PART 4: THE GOOD OF BRITAIN

Q3. Which Queen led an uprising against the occupying Roman forces?

....

Q4. Which 9th century king successfully defended his kingdom against the Vikings?

....

Q5. Who was the nurse who became a heroine of the Crimean War?

....

Q6. Who was the heroine who helped to save 13 people from the wreck of the SS Forfarshire?

....

PART 4: THE GOOD OF BRITAIN

Q7. Which Scottish campaigner for women's rights also pioneered birth control?

....

Q8. Which politician campaigned for the abolition of slavery?

....

Q9. Who was the scholar and writer who defied Henry VIII's supremacy over the Pope and was executed for his opposition?

....

Q10. Which soldier founded the Boy Scouts in 1908?

....

PART 4: THE BAD OF BRITAIN

Q1. Which of the Great Train Robbers escaped from prison and fled to Australia and then Brazil?

....

Q2. Perhaps he wasn't a bad person, but Albert Pierrepoint had a macabre occupation. What was it?

....

Q3. He is probably Britain's most notorious prisoner and is known by the same name as one of the Magnificent Seven. Who is he?

....

PART 4: THE BAD OF BRITAIN

Q4. Who was the notorious 18th century highwayman executed for his crimes in 1739?

....

Q5. By what name was the infamous 18th century pirate Edward Teach known?

....

Q6. Who was the trader whose fraudulent dealings brought down Barings Bank in 1995?

....

Q7. Which traitor was hanged, drawn and quartered in 1606 for the crime he planned to commit?

....

PART 4: THE BAD OF BRITAIN

Q8. Who was the musician who invaded the stage at the 1996 Brit Awards?

....

Q9. Which army officer was instrumental in the massacre of the MacDonalds at Glencoe?

....

Q10. Which notorious robber and drug dealer was jailed for life for the murder of Stephen Cameron in 1996?

....

Part 5
GREAT BRITISH INVENTORS

All of these great Brits made headlines in their day. What did they invent that was so special? We've given a clue to help you work it out!

Q1. Percy Shaw – motorists depend upon them

....

Q2. Alexander Fleming – improved the health of everyone

....

PART 5: GREAT BRITISH INVENTORS

Q3. Robert Watson Watt – said to have helped win World War II

....

Q4. Jethro Tull – great advance in agriculture

....

Q5. James Hargreaves – revolutionary industrial invention

....

Q6. John Logie Baird – every home has one nowadays

....

PART 5: GREAT BRITISH INVENTORS

Q7. Edwin Budding – his name might give
a clue to this appliance

....

Q8. Richard Trevithick – pioneered
inter-city travel

....

Q9. Arthur Wynne – puzzling creation!

....

Q10. James Dewar – handy thing to take
on a picnic

....

PART 5: GREAT BRITISH INVENTORS

Q11. Christopher Cockerell – rapid cross-Channel transport

....

Q12. Frank Whittle – revolutionised flying

....

Q13. Barnes Wallis – used by the Dambusters

....

Q14. Rowland Hill – they are stuck on every day!

....

PART 5: GREAT BRITISH INVENTORS

Q15. John Kay – misleading name,
but used in cotton mills

....

Q16. Sir Henry Cole – most of us send
them once a year

....

Q17. Charles Babbage – an invention that
has changed the world

....

PART 5: GREAT BRITISH INVENTORS

Q18. Tim Berners-Lee – it is everywhere, all around the world

....

Q19. James Dyson – everyday household cleaning appliance

....

Q20. James Henry Atkinson – pest controller!

....

GREAT
BRITISH

CELEBS ▶▶

Part 1

BRITISH CELEBS IN THE NEWS IN 2012

Q1. Which TV and radio presenter announced she was pregnant by her boyfriend Jesse Wood?

....

Q2. Jesse Wood is the son of which ageing rocker?

....

Q3. Who did singer Thomas Cohen marry in the Kent village of Davington?

....

▶▶▶

PART 1: BRITISH CELEBS 2012

Q4. Which pop singer is married to painter Sam Cooper and announced she is pregnant with her second child?

....

Q5. Who gave birth to her daughter Hollie but didn't see her for three days due to being critically ill?

....

Q6. Which British actor split from his actress girlfriend Kristen Stewart?

....

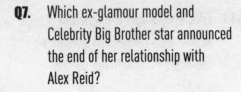

PART 1: BRITISH CELEBS 2012

Q7. Which ex-glamour model and Celebrity Big Brother star announced the end of her relationship with Alex Reid?

....

Q8. American Ayda Field flew into London to give birth in the UK. Who is her singer husband?

....

Q9. It was rumoured that Simon Cowell had a fling with which former X Factor judge?

....

PART 1: BRITISH CELEBS 2012

Q10. Who was divorced from Katy Perry after a brief marriage lasting only 14 months?

....

Q11. Which former glamour model became engaged to male model and TV presenter Leandro Penna only to split up a few months later?

....

Q12. Which actress became engaged to musician James Righton?

....

Q13. Which comedian won Celebrity Big Brother in September, 2012?

....

PART 1: BRITISH CELEBS 2012

Q14. Lila Grace is the daughter of which supermodel?

....

Q15. English actor and model Hugh Dancy is married to which star of the hit American TV show Homeland?

....

Q16. Who bought a £7 million mansion in West Sussex with her boyfriend Simon Konecki?

....

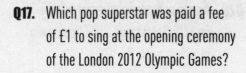

PART 1: BRITISH CELEBS 2012

Q17. Which pop superstar was paid a fee of £1 to sing at the opening ceremony of the London 2012 Olympic Games?

....

Q18. Katherine Jenkins denied reports of an alleged affair with which celebrity?

....

Q19. Who caused controversy by stating on TV that 'striking workers should be shot'?

....

PART 1: BRITISH CELEBS 2012

Q20. A charity fundraising event was held on 14th September, 2012 in memory of which singer?

....

Q21. Model Jacqui Ainsley became engaged to which British film director in October, 2012?

....

Q22. Cheryl Cole left as a judge on which American TV show amid accusations her accent was too strong and couldn't be understood?

....

PART 1: BRITISH CELEBS 2012

Q23. Who expressed concern about her own topless antics in 2012's first Celebrity Big Brother show?

....

Q24. Which former Pop Idol contestant and pop star split from his wife of four years in October, 2012?

....

Q25. Which girl band announced a 10th anniversary comeback at a London press conference in October, 2012?

....

Part 2

GREAT BRITISH MOVIE STARS

From the short description of each star, can you work out the names of these great British movie stars?

Q1. Actor famed for his Shakespearean roles, notably Hamlet in 1948

....

Q2. Ten-time BAFTA-winning actress whose movies include Casino Royale and Mrs Brown

....

▶▶▶

PART 2: BRITISH MOVIE STARS

Q3. Not a lot of people know that he was born Maurice Micklewhite

....

Q4. Suave actor whose big screen successes include The Pink Panther

....

Q5. Actress who co-starred with Clark Gable in Gone with the Wind

....

Q6. Actor whose roles have included a Russian submarine commander, a Chicago cop and a spy!

....

▶▶▶

PART 2: BRITISH MOVIE STARS

Q7. Oscar-winning actress and star of Mary Poppins and The Sound of Music

....

Q8. Actor who played Pip in the original Great Expectations

....

Q9. Welsh actor famed for his roles in Hannibal and The Silence of the Lambs

....

Q10. Oscar-winning actor and star of The King's Speech

....

PART 2: BRITISH MOVIE STARS

Q11. Actor known for his roles in epics such as Ben-Hur and Zulu

....

Q12. Actress who won the Best Actress Oscar for her performance in The Reader

....

Q13. Actor forever remembered for playing eight characters in Kind Hearts and Coronets

....

Q14. Actress whose more recent films include Brighton Rock and Red

....

PART 2: BRITISH MOVIE STARS

Q15. Actor who played Alfie in the 2004 remake of the film of the same name

....

Q16. Star of Notting Hill and Four Weddings and a Funeral

....

Q17. Actress who played Sylvia McCordle in Gosford Park

....

Q18. Actor who played George Smiley in the 2011 film Tinker Tailor Soldier Spy

....

PART 2: BRITISH MOVIE STARS

Q19. Actress who played Elizabeth Swann in the Pirates of the Caribbean movies

....

Q20. Veteran actor typecast for his roles in vampire films

....

Q21. Actor who appeared in Lock, Stock and Two Smoking Barrels and Snatch

....

Q22. Much-loved TV and film actress who starred in the 1983 film Educating Rita

....

▶▶▶

PART 2: BRITISH MOVIE STARS

Q23. Actor who played Gandalf in the Lord of the Rings trilogy

....

Q24. Actor who starred with Liam Neeson in the Oscar-winning Schindler's List

....

Q25. Actress who played Queen Elizabeth in The King's Speech

....

Part 3

GREAT BRITISH POP STARS

These questions are about the pick of the greatest British pop stars of all time. How many can you get right?

Q1. Which group sold over a million with their 1998 re-release of an old Bee Gees hit?

....

Q2. What was the Beatles' first British no.1 hit single?

....

PART 3: BRITISH POP STARS

Q3. What single did David Bowie take to the no.1 spot in 1980?

....

Q4. Who sold over a million with his own version of Unchained Melody in 2002?

....

Q5. Which group had a million selling hit single in 1976 with Save Your Kisses for Me?

....

Q6. Which group, led by Ray Davies, had three UK no.1 hit singles in the 1960s?

....

▶▶▶

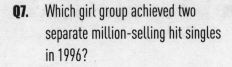

PART 3: BRITISH POP STARS

Q7. Which girl group achieved two separate million-selling hit singles in 1996?

....

Q8. Which John Lennon song was voted in one poll as the best pop song of all time?

....

Q9. Which duo, who made their names in TV's Soldier, Soldier, hit the top of the charts twice in 1995, both becoming million-selling hit singles?

....

PART 3: BRITISH POP STARS

Q10. What was the biggest-selling single of 1975?

....

Q11. A revival of which singer's music saw a re-release of (Is This the Way To) Amarillo shoot to number 1 in 2005 and sell over a million records?

....

Q12. Which British pop icon is the only singer to have achieved UK no.1 hits in six consecutive decades, from the 50s to the 00s?

....

PART 3: BRITISH POP STARS

Q13. How many UK no.1 singles did The Beatles achieve?

....

Q14. Whose first single Smile went to no.1 in 2006?

....

Q15. Which group achieved 14 British top 10 hits between 1981 and 2004?

....

Q16. Which group was formed by Chris Martin and Jonny Buckland in 1996 and had their first British no.1 in 2008?

....

PART 3: BRITISH POP STARS

Q17. Which group celebrated their 50th anniversary in the summer of 2012?

....

Q18. Which British superstar, though active since the 1960s, didn't have his first solo British no.1 until 1990?

....

Q19. George Michael, who had six no.1 hits between 1984 and 1996, had his first solo no.1 with which song?

....

PART 3: BRITISH POP STARS

Q20. Who had the biggest-selling single of 2011 with Someone Like You?

....

Q21. Which former Pop Idol winner went on to have UK no.1 hits with four of his first five singles?

....

Q22. Which Scottish group, who had three British no.1 hits, reformed in 2004 after a split lasting several years?

....

PART 3: BRITISH POP STARS

Q23. Which British band, with eight no.1 singles, was formed in Manchester in 1991 as The Rain?

....

Q24. What was Take That's first single, a no.1 hit, when they reformed in 2006?

....

Q25. Which British girl group had 13 top 10 hits, including the no.1 hit Whole Again?

....

Part 4

GREAT BRITISH TV STARS

These questions are about some of the most iconic British TV stars of all time.

Q1. William Roache has played which soap character since 1960?

....

Q2. John Cleese starred in which cult comedy series which ran from 1975-1979?

....

▶▶▶

PART 4: BRITISH TV STARS

Q3. Which actor's TV credits include Only Fools and Horses, Darling Buds of May and A Touch of Frost?

....

Q4. Who played David Brent in a mockumentary based in a paper company's office in Slough?

....

Q5. Which grumpy character played by Richard Wilson uttered the catchphrase 'I don't believe it!"

....

PART 4: BRITISH TV STARS

Q6. Which actress played the snobbish Hyacinth Bucket in Keeping up Appearances?

....

Q7. Who played Miss Brahms in Are You Being Served, before going on to star in the soap Eastenders?

....

Q8. The Reverend Geraldine Granger, played by Dawn French, was better known as whom?

....

PART 4: BRITISH TV STARS

Q9. What was the name of Ronnie Barker's stuttering shopkeeper in Open All Hours?

....

Q10. Who has appeared as the eponymous Doc Martin and also as Gary Strang in Men Behaving Badly?

....

Q11. Which much-loved actor starred in the Inspector Morse series and earlier in the ITV police series The Sweeney?

....

Q12. Which actress, who started out in Brookside, later had leading roles in Peak Practice and Silent Witness?

....

Q13. From Fusilier Dave Tucker in Soldier Soldier to Dr. Tony Hill in Wire in the Blood – who is this popular actor?

....

Q14. What was the name of Helen Mirren's character in Lynda La Plante's brilliant series Prime Suspect?

....

Q15. Which Scottish actor played DI Rebus based on the books by Ian Rankin?

....

Q16. Up to and including 2012, which actor has played Doctor Who on TV for the longest period?

....

Q17. Which married couple presented TV chat shows from 1988 to 2009?

....

PART 4: BRITISH TV STARS

Q18. Which popular actor played private detective Eddie Shoestring in 1979 before later starring in Waking the Dead?

....

Q19. She has starred in Brookside, The Royle Family and more recently appeared in Coronation Street. Who is this versatile actress?

....

Q20. Which actress has played Cindy Beale in Eastenders and Stella Price in Coronation Street?

....

PART 4: BRITISH TV STARS

Q21. Which comedian and actor starred as Jonathan Creek in the crime drama series of that name?

....

Q22. What was occupation of Ronnie Corbett's character Timothy in the TV comedy Sorry!?

....

Q23. Which acting 'Dame' stars in Downton Abbey as the Dowager Countess of Grantham?

....

PART 4: BRITISH TV STARS

Q24. Who are the three stars who have presented the game show Blankety Blank?

....

Q25. How were James Bolam and Rodney Bewes known on screen?

....

British Number Ones

GREAT
BRITISH

Stonehenge .... James Bond .... Downton Abbey .... O2 Arena

LIFE ▷▷

Television & Soaps

Part 1

GONE BUT NOT FORGOTTEN

All these people passed away in 2012. How many can you identify from the brief descriptions given? Some were British, others not, but they are all recognisable names.

Q1. Singer who had eleven US no.1 hit singles

....

Q2. First man to walk on the Moon

....

PART 1: GONE BUT NOT FORGOTTEN

Q3. Founding member of the Bee Gees

....

Q4. Much-loved English comedian and actor

....

Q5. Former member of the pop dance troupe Pan's People

....

Q6. Irish author whose novels included Light a Penny Candle

....

PART 1: GONE BUT NOT FORGOTTEN

Q7. Actor who won a Best Actor Oscar for his role in Marty

....

Q8. Fantasy and horror author who wrote Fahrenheit 451

....

Q9. Legendary host of the American TV show American Bandstand

....

Q10. Long-time presenter of the American TV show Soul Train

....

PART 1: GONE BUT NOT FORGOTTEN

Q11. Actress, comedienne and pianist born in 1917

....

Q12. Song-writer who composed the score for The Way We Were and Sting

....

Q13. Actress who starred in the 1943 Broadway musical Oklahoma!

....

Q14. Grammy award-winning jazz and gospel singer

....

PART 1: GONE BUT NOT FORGOTTEN

Q15. Former member of The Monkees who once appeared in Coronation Street

....

Q16. One-time member of hard rock bands Deep Purple and Whitesnake

....

Q17. Founder and leader of the Unification Church

....

PART 1: GONE BUT NOT FORGOTTEN

Q18. Astronaut who became the first American woman in space in 1983

....

Q19. 60s icon who founded a multi-million dollar hair products business

....

Q20. Film director whose works included Top Gun and Enemy of the State

....

PART 1: GONE BUT NOT FORGOTTEN

Q21. 'Queen of Disco' whose 70s hits included I Feel Love

....

Q22. Prolific American novelist and frequent talk show guest

....

Q23. Singer who had a 60s hit with San Francisco (Be Sure to Wear Flowers in Your Hair)

....

Q24. Legendary editor-in-chief of Cosmopolitan magazine for more than 30 years

....

PART 1: GONE BUT NOT FORGOTTEN

Q25. Film producer who won an Academy Award for Driving Miss Daisy

....

Q26. Screenwriter and director whose work included Sleepless in Seattle

....

Q27. Rapper who co-founded The Beastie Boys in the early 1980s

....

PART 1: GONE BUT NOT FORGOTTEN

Q28. English singer, comedian and actor
and ex-presenter of Family Fortunes

....

Q29. American film and TV actor who
appeared in The Big Lebowski and
Road House

....

Q30. Lyricist famous for his prolific
song-writing partnership with Burt
Bacharach

....

Part 2

BRITISH No.1s OF 2012

The following were some of the biggest-selling British no.1 hits of 2012. Can you name the artist or artists who had these hits? All of the artists are British!

Q1. Paradise

....

Q2. Hot Right Now

....

PART 2: BRITISH No.1s OF 2012

Q3. Domino

....

Q4. Young

....

Q5. Sing

....

Q6. Call My Name

....

PART 2: BRITISH No.1s OF 2012

Q7. Spectrum (Say My Name)

....

Q8. How We Do (Party)

....

Q9. Bom Bom

....

Q10. Wings

....

PART 2: BRITISH No.1s ALBUMS 2012

Now, try the same for some of the biggest-selling British no.1 albums of 2012.

Q1. +

....

Q2. 21

....

Q3. Our Version of Events

....

PART 2: BRITISH No.1s ALBUMS 2012

Q4. In My Dreams

....

Q5. Sonik Kicks

....

Q6. Electra Heart

....

Q7. Strangeland

....

▶▶▶

PART 2: BRITISH No.1s ALBUMS 2012

Q8. ill Manors

....

Q9. Come of Age

....

Q10. Contrast

....

Part 3

20 BRITISH MOVIES OF 2012

The best movies of 2012, not all British-made but if not, with British actors. Here are the clues.

Q1. British politician who was the subject of the biopic The Iron Lady

....

Q2. The latest James Bond film released in 2012

....

▶▶▶

PART 3: BRITISH MOVIES OF 2012

Q3. The full name of the hotel whose guests included Judi Dench and Bill Nighy

....

Q4. Cameron Diaz's Oscar-winning co-star in the comedy Gambit

....

Q5. Actor knight who stars in the epic fantasy Hobbit: An Unexpected Journey

....

Q6. Musical drama starring Hugh Jackman and Russell Crowe

....

PART 3: BRITISH MOVIES OF 2012

Q7. Big screen version of a popular 70s TV series, starring Ray Winstone

....

Q8. Ex-Harry Potter actor who stars in the supernatural thriller The Woman in Black

....

Q9. Fantasy sequel starring Ralph Fiennes and Liam Neeson

....

Q10. Gangster film starring Scottish actor John Hannah

....

PART 3: BRITISH MOVIES OF 2012

Q11. Drug smuggling thriller starring Kate Beckinsale

....

Q12. Roman drama starring and directed by Ralph Fiennes

....

Q13. First World War cavalry drama starring Emily Watson and Benedict Cumberbatch

....

Q14. Mystery about a missing woman, starring Daniel Craig and Christopher Plummer

....

PART 3: BRITISH MOVIES OF 2012

Q15. Batman sequel starring Christian Bale

....

Q16. Mob thriller starring Bruce Willis and Emily Blunt

....

Q17. Fantasy movie starring Hugh Jackman

....

Q18. Rom-com starring Keira Knightley

....

PART 3: BRITISH MOVIES OF 2012

Q19. Director of the 2012 comedy A Fantastic Fear of Everything

....

Q20. Modern urban drama starring Jamie Foreman and Zoe Tapper

....

Part 4

GREAT BRITISH SIGHTS

From the descriptions given, can you work out what these famous British tourist attractions are?

Q1. Castle on the Thames, on which construction work began in the 11th century

....

Q2. Location of the wedding of Prince Charles and Lady Diana Spencer in 1981

....

PART 4: GREAT BRITISH SIGHTS

Q3. Home of the world's largest collection of living plants

....

Q4. Cornwall's main tourist attraction which houses the world's largest greenhouse

....

Q5. Largest Gothic cathedral in northern Europe

....

Q6. Northern landmark modelled on the Eiffel Tower

....

PART 4: GREAT BRITISH SIGHTS

Q7. The most visited modern art gallery in the world

....

Q8. Staffordshire theme park, one of the most popular in Europe

....

Q9. Fortress overlooking Scotland's capital city

....

Q10. World Heritage Site in Northern Ireland comprising of more than 40,000 basalt columns

....

PART 4: GREAT BRITISH SIGHTS

Q11. Once a white elephant, now one of the world's premier concert venues

....

Q12. Prehistoric monument in Wiltshire, one of the oldest in the world

....

Q13. Former royal palace built as a seaside retreat for the future King George IV

....

PART 4: GREAT BRITISH SIGHTS

Q14. Popular holiday destination also associated with the poets Wordsworth, Coleridge and Southey

....

Q15. Children's theme park situated near Windsor

....

Q16. Attraction first opened in London in 1835 as a museum

....

PART 4: GREAT BRITISH SIGHTS

Q17. Royal residence on the Thames last resided in by George II

....

Q18. The main home, in Kent, of Winston Churchill until his death in 1965

....

Q19. Partially ruined building on the site of a famous 1066 conflict

....

Q20. Tower atop a hill near Stirling built to commemorate a 13th century Scottish hero

....

Part 5

GREAT BRITISH SOAPS

The nation loves a good soap opera and Britain still has a few long-running soaps. See if you can remember some of the events from the country's most popular soaps, starting with Eastenders...

Q1. Which character was murdered by teenager Ben Mitchell?

....

Q2. Who returned to Eastenders in August, 2012 after a six-year absence?

....

▶▶▶

PART 5: SOAPS – EASTENDERS

Q3. Who disappeared and was found sleeping rough in an underpass?

....

Q4. Who did Kat kick out of the Queen Vic over missing stock and cash?

....

Q5. Alice received some flowers mistakenly sent to her, apparently from Anthony. Who was the intended recipient?

....

Q6. Where did Shirley propose to Phil?

....

PART 5: SOAPS – EASTENDERS

Q7. Who helped Lucy to pay off some of Ian's debts?

....

Q8. Which actress previously played Michelle Fowler?

....

Q9. What is the name of the fictional borough in which Eastenders is set?

....

Q10. Which Eastenders actor had a no.1 hit in 1986 with Every Loser Wins?

....

PART 5: SOAPS – CORONATION STREET

Q1. Which 'bad boy' character returned briefly to the Street in 2012?

....

Q2. Who did Rita marry in June, 2012?

....

Q3. Who is the fireman with whom Eileen Grimshaw fell in love?

....

Q4. What is the name of Carla Connor's brother who was released from prison and came to work in Underworld?

....

▶▶▶

PART 5: SOAPS – CORONATION STREET

Q5. Peter Barlow caused a fight at Simon's birthday party because Nick and Leanne had bought him what present?

....

Q6. Sunita agreed to take money from Dev's account so that her boyfriend Karl could buy what?

....

Q7. What is the name of Tyrone and Kirsty's new baby?

....

PART 5: SOAPS – CORONATION STREET

Q8. What is the name of the all-female taxi firm for whom Steve's ex Tracy went to work?

....

Q9. How much money did Jeff Horton leave to Tommy Duckworth in his will?

....

Q10. What are the names of Owen's two daughters?

....

PART 5: SOAPS – BEST OF THE REST

Q1. In which city is the soap Hollyoaks set?

....

Q2. What first for a British soap did Hollyoaks introduce in 2009?

....

Q3. Which Hollyoaks character, played by Ashley Slanina-Davies, left the show in August, 2012?

....

Q4. Which soap is set in fictional Summer Bay?

....

PART 5: SOAPS – BEST OF THE REST

Q5. Which soap, set in the fictional town of Los Barcos, was scrapped after only a year on our screens?

....

Q6. Which soap, originally screened for the first time in 1964, was briefly revived in 2001 after a 13-year absence?

....

Q7. Which medical drama was first shown in 1986 and was still being screened in 2012?

....

PART 5: SOAPS – BEST OF THE REST

Q8. What spin-off from Casualty was first aired on TV in 1999?

....

Q9. In which year was Emmerdale Farm first shown on TV?

....

Q10. In which year did Emmerdale Farm change its name to Emmerdale?

....

ANSWERS

ANSWERS

GREAT BRITISH ROYALS

PART 1: JUBILEE AND THE QUEEN

Q1.	1953
Q2.	The Epsom Derby
Q3.	Spirit of Chartwell
Q4.	Outside Buckingham Palace
Q5.	2012 (though over 4000 were lit around the world)
Q6.	St. Paul's Cathedral
Q7.	21st April
Q8.	There is no set date, but it is usually the 1st, 2nd or 3rd Saturday in June
Q9.	1926
Q10.	Queen Victoria
Q11.	Mayfair, London (Bruton Street)
Q12.	Alexandra Mary
Q13.	Windsor Great Park
Q14.	12
Q15.	Winston Churchill
Q16.	Two – Pope John Paul II and Pope Benedict XVI
Q17.	The Royal Yacht Britannia
Q18.	Palace of Holyroodhouse, Edinburgh
Q19.	The official website for the British Monarchy
Q20.	1947

ANSWERS

PART 2: WILLS & KATE

Q1.	1982
Q2.	Middleton
Q3.	Westminster Abbey
Q4.	29th April, 2011
Q5.	Website designer and photographer
Q6.	Her parents' business, Party Pieces
Q7.	Pippa and James
Q8.	Household Cavalry (Blues and Royals)
Q9.	Captain
Q10.	Earl of Strathearn and Baron Carrickfergus
Q11.	Falkland Islands
Q12.	Hockey
Q13.	Marlborough
Q14.	Reading
Q15.	Belize
Q16.	St Mary's Hospital, Paddington
Q17.	Flight Lieutenant Wales
Q18.	Michael and Carole
Q19.	Jigsaw Junior
Q20.	South East Asia and the South Pacific

PART 3: CHARLES & CAMILLA

Q1.	Shand
Q2.	Philip Arthur George
Q3.	Caernarfon Castle
Q4.	Air Chief Marshal
Q5.	Birkhall
Q6.	Dame Grand Cross of the Royal Victorian Order (GCVO)
Q7.	Timbertop
Q8.	The Guildhall, Windsor
Q9.	Nine
Q10.	Cheam
Q11.	Rosemary
Q12.	The Prince's Trust
Q13.	Duke of Rothesay
Q14.	Ich Dien (I Serve)
Q15.	White (or silver)
Q16.	Cook for the Queen
Q17.	Edward, son of George V and Mary (later King Edward VIII)
Q18.	Buckingham Palace
Q19.	Trinity College
Q20.	Admiral of the Fleet

PART 4: REST OF THE ROYALS

Q1.	Earl of Wessex (and also Viscount Severn)	**Q21.**	Henry Charles Albert David
Q2.	Countess of Wessex (Edward's wife)	**Q22.**	Captain
Q3.	Duke of York	**Q23.**	Nicholas I of Russia
Q4.	Earl of Inverness and Baron Killyleagh	**Q24.**	Chelsy Davy
Q5.	Princess Royal	**Q25.**	Clarence House
Q6.	Gatcombe Park, Gloucestershire	**Q26.**	Apache helicopters
Q7.	Cousin (also cousin to the Duke of Edinburgh)	**Q27.**	Corfu
Q8.	Katharine Worsley	**Q28.**	His nephew
Q9.	Kensington Palace	**Q29.**	1921
Q10.	Mountbatten-Windsor	**Q30.**	Queen Victoria
Q11.	Princess Beatrice (5th in line)	**Q31.**	Commander
Q12.	Ardent Productions	**Q32.**	The Duke of Edinburgh's Award
Q13.	BBC Sports Personality of the Year	**Q33.**	He was the first member of the Royal Family to be interviewed on television
Q14.	Angus Ogilvy	**Q34.**	Earl of Merioneth and Baron Greenwich
Q15.	Westminster Abbey	**Q35.**	Four – all older sisters
Q16.	Princess Michael of Kent	**Q36.**	Gordonstoun
Q17.	15th September, 1984	**Q37.**	Autumn Kelly
Q18.	Eton College	**Q38.**	Viscount Linley
Q19.	Polo and rugby	**Q39.**	Duke of Gloucester
Q20.	Lesotho	**Q40.**	Castle of Mey (in Caithness)

PART 5: PAST BRITISH MONARCHS

Q1. King James I (James VI of Scotland)

Q2. Interregnum (Charles I had been executed and Oliver Cromwell ruled)

Q3. Queen Anne

Q4. George III

Q5. William IV

Q6. 1837

Q7. Edward VII

Q8. George V (in 1932)

Q9. Duke of Windsor

Q10. The Queen Mother

Q11. Charles II

Q12. William of Orange

Q13. The succession of any monarch who was not a Protestant

Q14. George IV

Q15. Danish

Q16. George I

Q17. George V

Q18. Richard I

Q19. Catherine Parr

Q20. Bonnie Prince Charlie, claimant to the Scottish throne

GREAT BRITISH SPORT

PART 1: 2012 OLYMPICS

Q1.	65		**Q14.**	Roger Federer
Q2.	29		**Q15.**	Laura Robson
Q3.	David Greene		**Q16.**	Alistair and Jonathan Brownlee
Q4.	Mo Farah		**Q17.**	Nicola Adams
Q5.	Greg Rutherford		**Q18.**	Super heavyweight
Q6.	Women's 400m freestyle & Women's 800m freestyle		**Q19.**	Pommel horse
Q7.	Jason Kenny		**Q20.**	Elizabeth Tweddle
Q8.	Sir Chris Hoy			

OLYMPIC VENUES

Q9.	Edward Clancy		**Q21a**	Cycling (road)
Q10.	Keirin		**Q21b**	Football
Q11.	Laura Trott		**Q21c**	Volleyball
Q12.	Helen Glover		**Q21d**	Rowing & canoeing
Q13.	Women's double sculls		**Q21e**	Equestrian & modern pentathlon

PART 2: PARALYMPICS

Q1.	Third, behind China and Russia
Q2.	120
Q3.	34
Q4.	Sarah Storey
Q5.	David Weir
Q6.	Equestrianism
Q7.	Women's 400m freestyle and women's 200m individual medley
Q8.	Natasha Baker
Q9.	Hannah Cockroft
Q10.	Swimming
Q11.	Cycling
Q12.	Men's 200m individual medley
Q13.	Archery
Q14.	Eleven
Q15.	Jonnie Peacock
Q16.	Judo
Q17.	Zoe Newson
Q18.	Mixed coxed four
Q19.	39
Q20.	Women's doubles and mixed quad doubles
Q21.	Seven
Q22.	Jessica-Jane Applegate
Q23.	Men's 100m backstroke S7
Q24.	Sailing (mixed single-person keelboat)
Q25.	Men's discus throw F42

PART 3: BRITISH SPORTING EVENTS

Q1.	Roger Federer	Q11.	1839, though it was unofficially run three years earlier
Q2.	Serena Williams	Q12.	University Boat Race
Q3.	Jonathan Marray	Q13.	The Derby
Q4.	Samantha Stosur (the 2011 champion)	Q14.	Yorkshire (31, including one shared)
Q5.	Heather Watson	Q15.	Five – Carnoustie, Muirfield, St. Andrews, Troon, Turnberry
Q6.	Anne Keothavong and Elena Baltacha	Q16.	The Henley Royal Regatta
Q7.	Novak Djokovic	Q17.	English Greyhound Derby
Q8.	Novak Djokovic	Q18.	Cowes, Isle of Wight (Cowes Week)
Q9.	David Ferrer	Q19.	Twickenham (82,000)
Q10.	James Ward	Q20.	Aintree, Brooklands, Brands Hatch and Silverstone

PART 4: FOOTBALL

Q1.	Liverpool
Q2.	Cardiff City
Q3.	Reading, Southampton and West Ham United
Q4.	Steve Bruce
Q5.	Rangers
Q6.	Robin van Persie (Arsenal)
Q7.	Alan Pardew (Newcastle United)
Q8.	Wolves, Blackburn Rovers and Bolton Wanderers
Q9.	Dundee
Q10.	Swansea City
Q11.	Doncaster Rovers, Coventry City and Portsmouth
Q12.	Rickie Lambert
Q13.	Portsmouth
Q14.	Birmingham City, Blackpool and Cardiff City
Q15.	Dunfermline Athletic

Q16.	Charlton Athletic
Q17.	Sheffield United, Huddersfield Town, Milton Keynes Dons and Stevenage
Q18.	Huddersfield Town (defeated Sheffield United 8-7 on penalties)
Q19.	Jordan Rhodes
Q20.	Wycombe Wanderers, Chesterfield, Exeter City and Rochdale

EURO 2012

Q1.	Ukraine and Poland
Q2.	Italy
Q3.	Ukraine
Q4.	Joleon Lescott
Q5.	France
Q6.	Seven
Q7.	Germany and Portugal
Q8.	16
Q9.	Kiev
Q10.	Keith Andrews

PART 5: GENERAL SPORT

Q1.	Frankel	Q16.	Ferrari
Q2.	Camelot (completing the 2000 Guineas & Derby double)	Q17.	Pastor Maldonado
Q3.	Neptune Collonges	Q18.	Mark Webber
Q4.	Its name was WAS!	Q19.	McLaren-Mercedes
Q5.	A.P. McCoy	Q20.	Russia
Q6.	Wales	Q21.	Adrian Lewis
Q7.	Scotland	Q22.	Christian Kist (Netherlands)
Q8.	$14\frac{1}{2} - 13\frac{1}{2}$	Q23.	Ronnie O'Sullivan
Q9.	Harlequins	Q24.	New York Giants
Q10.	Warrington Wolves and Leeds Rhinos (Warrington winning 35-18)	Q25.	Danny Garcia
Q11.	Ernie Els	Q26.	Bradley Wiggins
Q12.	Rory McIlory	Q27.	Andrew Strauss
Q13.	Bubba Watson	Q28.	England won 2-0 with the other Test drawn
Q14.	Webb Simpson	Q29.	Warwickshire
Q15.	Royal Lytham & St. Annes	Q30.	Mark Cavendish

GREAT BRITISH HEADLINE MAKERS

PART 1: BRITISH POLITICS

Q1.	A referendum on Scottish independence	Q11.	Liam Fox
Q2.	Chris Huhne	Q12.	Andy Coulson
Q3.	He was charged with common assault following a disturbance in a House of Commons bar	Q13.	Peter Mandelson
Q4.	George Galloway, for the Respect Party	Q14.	The apology was because of his U-turn on university tuition fees
Q5.	Vince Cable	Q15.	Kenneth Clarke
Q6.	Daily Telegraph	Q16.	Jeremy Hunt
Q7.	William Hague	Q17.	David Miliband
Q8.	Witney	Q18.	They made him get off his bike and exit Downing Street by a different gate
Q9.	Peter Robinson	Q19.	Nigel Farage
Q10.	David Laws	Q20.	Six

PART 2: NEWS STORIES...AT HOME

Q1.	Lord Justice Leveson
Q2.	Rebekah Brooks
Q3.	Rupert and James Murdoch
Q4.	They were convicted of murdering Stephen Lawrence in 1993
Q5.	Fred Goodwin
Q6.	The Sun on Sunday
Q7.	Chelmsford, Perth and St Asaph
Q8.	Dr. Rowan Williams, Archbishop of Canterbury
Q9.	60p and 50p respectively
Q10.	The sinking of the Titanic
Q11.	The Olympic Flame
Q12.	She became the first female Commander of a warship
Q13.	Barclays
Q14.	George Entwistle
Q15.	The Shard
Q16.	First Group
Q17.	Asil Nadir
Q18.	Tesco
Q19.	Ecuador
Q20.	It marked the Queen's 60th anniversary of her accession to the British throne

ANSWERS

PART 2: NEWS STORIES...AND ABROAD

Q1.	Dogs
Q2.	Paul Ryan
Q3.	Canary Islands
Q4.	Standard Chartered
Q5.	For making a musical, political protest in a church
Q6.	Euro 2012 football championships
Q7.	It is the name of the science laboratory that landed on Mars and began sending back photographs
Q8.	Mecca, Saudi Arabia
Q9.	A football match in Egypt
Q10.	Athens
Q11.	Vladimir Putin
Q12.	He allegedly murdered 17 Afghan civilians in a gun rampage
Q13.	Costa Concordia
Q14.	Francois Hollande
Q15.	Hosni Mubarak, former President of Egypt
Q16.	India
Q17.	Hurricane Isaac
Q18.	Libya
Q19.	Italy
Q20.	Pierre-Auguste Renoir

PART 3: ODD AND FUNNY STORIES

Q1.	964	**Q11.**	That he is too fat to be executed (he is 34 stone)
Q2.	A duck called Star who accompanies his owner on his charitable trips!	**Q12.**	His pet dog, who jumped up for a cuddle accidentally setting off the gun
Q3.	Dog – he is a Great Dane who stands 7ft 4ins on his hind legs	**Q13.**	$40,000 in cash, hidden in capsules
Q4.	$7 million worth of gold hidden in the garage!	**Q14.**	Deep-fried Mars Bars! The confectionery giant won't support the application on health grounds
Q5.	Her sense of smell and taste	**Q15.**	A British soldier gave birth and didn't know she was pregnant!
Q6.	Most cheerful car park in Britain – it displays jokes and brainteasers on the walls	**Q16.**	Nick Clegg
Q7.	Oakley was only 15 months old – the letter was sent to him by mistake	**Q17.**	Puzzles, including crosswords and jigsaws
Q8.	King Richard III	**Q18.**	Onion
Q9.	Jumbo-sized fizzy drinks	**Q19.**	He tweeted the information on Twitter!
Q10.	Reputedly, that only 'cranks' claim to have seen UFOs	**Q20.**	57th version

PART 4: THE GOOD AND THE BAD OF BRITAIN...

...THE GOOD

Q1.	Robin Hood
Q2.	Rob Roy MacGregor
Q3.	Boudica (alt. Boadicea)
Q4.	Alfred the Great
Q5.	Florence Nightingale
Q6.	Grace Darling
Q7.	Marie Stopes
Q8.	William Wilberforce
Q9.	Sir Thomas More
Q10.	Robert Baden-Powell

...THE BAD

Q11.	Ronnie Biggs
Q12.	He was a hangman who is believed to have executed hundreds of people
Q13.	Charles Bronson
Q14.	Dick Turpin
Q15.	Blackbeard
Q16.	Nick Leeson
Q17.	Guy Fawkes
Q18.	Jarvis Cocker
Q19.	Robert Campbell
Q20.	Kenneth Noye

PART 5: GREAT BRITISH INVENTORS

Q1.	Cat's eyes	Q11.	Hovercraft
Q2.	Penicillin	Q12.	Jet engine
Q3.	Radar	Q13.	Bouncing bomb
Q4.	Seed drill	Q14.	Adhesive postage stamp
Q5.	Spinning Jenny	Q15.	Flying shuttle
Q6.	Television	Q16.	Christmas cards
Q7.	Lawn mower	Q17.	Analogue computer
Q8.	Locomotive	Q18.	World Wide Web
Q9.	Crosswords	Q19.	Bagless vacuum cleaner
Q10.	Thermos flask	Q20.	Mouse trap

GREAT BRITISH CELEBRITIES

PART 1: BRITISH CELEBS IN THE NEWS IN 2012

Q1.	Fearne Cotton	Q14.	Kate Moss
Q2.	Ronnie Wood of the Rolling Stones	Q15.	Claire Danes
Q3.	Peaches Geldof	Q16.	Adele
Q4.	Lily Allen	Q17.	Paul McCartney
Q5.	Amanda Holden	Q18.	David Beckham
Q6.	Robert Pattinson	Q19.	Jeremy Clarkson
Q7.	Chantelle Houghton	Q20.	Amy Winehouse
Q8.	Robbie Williams	Q21.	Guy Ritchie
Q9.	Dannii Minogue	Q22.	X Factor USA
Q10.	Russell Brand	Q23.	Denise Welch
Q11.	Katie Price	Q24.	Gareth Gates
Q12.	Keira Knightley	Q25.	Girls Aloud
Q13.	Julian Clary		

PART 2: GREAT BRITISH MOVIE STARS

Q1.	Laurence Olivier		Q14.	Helen Mirren
Q2.	Dame Judi Dench		Q15.	Jude Law
Q3.	Michael Caine		Q16.	Hugh Grant
Q4.	David Niven		Q17.	Kristin Scott Thomas
Q5.	Vivien Leigh		Q18.	Gary Oldman
Q6.	Sean Connery		Q19.	Keira Knightley
Q7.	Julie Andrews		Q20.	Christopher Lee
Q8.	John Mills		Q21.	Jason Statham
Q9.	Anthony Hopkins		Q22.	Julie Walters
Q10.	Colin Firth		Q23.	Ian McKellen
Q11.	Jack Hawkins		Q24.	Ralph Fiennes
Q12.	Kate Winslet		Q25.	Helena Bonham Carter
Q13.	Alec Guinness			

PART 3: GREAT BRITISH POP STARS

Q1.	Steps (Tragedy)	**Q13.**	17
Q2.	From Me to You (1963)	**Q14.**	Lily Allen
Q3.	Ashes to Ashes	**Q15.**	Duran Duran
Q4.	Gareth Gates	**Q16.**	Coldplay
Q5.	Brotherhood of Man	**Q17.**	The Rolling Stones
Q6.	The Kinks	**Q18.**	Elton John (Sacrifice/Healing Hands)
Q7.	Spice Girls (Wannabe and 2 Become 1)	**Q19.**	Careless Whisper
Q8.	Imagine	**Q20.**	Adele
Q9.	Robson and Jerome (Unchained Melody and I Believe)	**Q21.**	Will Young
Q10.	Bye Bye Baby	**Q22.**	Wet Wet Wet
Q11.	Tony Christie	**Q23.**	Oasis
Q12.	Cliff Richard	**Q24.**	Patience
		Q25.	Atomic Kitten

PART 4: GREAT BRITISH TV STARS

Q1.	Ken Barlow (Coronation Street)
Q2.	Fawlty Towers
Q3.	David Jason
Q4.	Ricky Gervais
Q5.	Victor Meldrew (One Foot in the Grave)
Q6.	Patricia Routledge
Q7.	Wendy Richard
Q8.	The Vicar of Dibley
Q9.	Arkwright
Q10.	Martin Clunes
Q11.	John Thaw
Q12.	Amanda Burton
Q13.	Robson Green

Q14.	Jane Tennison
Q15.	Ken Stott
Q16.	Tom Baker (6 years, 9 months)
Q17.	Richard Madeley and Judy Finnigan (This Morning and Richard & Judy)
Q18.	Trevor Eve
Q19.	Sue Johnston
Q20.	Michelle Collins
Q21.	Alan Davies
Q22.	Librarian
Q23.	Dame Maggie Smith
Q24.	Terry Wogan, Les Dawson and Lily Savage
Q25.	The Likely Lads

GREAT BRITISH LIFE

PART 1: GONE BUT NOT FORGOTTEN

Q1.	Whitney Houston	Q16.	Jon Lord
Q2.	Neil Armstrong	Q17.	Sun Myung Moon
Q3.	Robin Gibb	Q18.	Sally Ride
Q4.	Eric Sykes	Q19.	Vidal Sassoon
Q5.	Louise Clarke	Q20.	Tony Scott
Q6.	Maeve Binchy	Q21.	Donna Summer
Q7.	Ernest Borgnine	Q22.	Gore Vidal
Q8.	Ray Bradbury	Q23.	Scott McKenzie
Q9.	Dick Clark	Q24.	Helen Gurley Brown
Q10.	Don Cornelius	Q25.	Richard D. Zanuck
Q11.	Phyllis Diller	Q26.	Nora Ephron
Q12.	Marvin Hamlisch	Q27.	Adam Yauch
Q13.	Celeste Holm	Q28.	Max Bygraves
Q14.	Etta James	Q29.	Ben Gazzara
Q15.	Davy Jones	Q30.	Hal David

PART 2: BRITISH NO.1s OF 2012...

...THE SINGLES

Q1.	Coldplay
Q2.	DJ Fresh featuring Rita Ora
Q3.	Jessie J
Q4.	Tulisa
Q5.	Gary Barlow and the Commonwealth Band
Q6.	Cheryl Cole
Q7.	Florence + The Machine
Q8.	Rita Ora
Q9.	Sam and The Womp
Q10.	Little Mix

...THE ALBUMS

Q11.	Ed Sheeran
Q12.	Adele
Q13.	Emeli Sande
Q14.	Military Wives
Q15.	Paul Weller
Q16.	Marina & The Diamonds
Q17.	Keane
Q18.	Plan B
Q19.	The Vaccines
Q20.	Conor Maynard

PART 3: 20 BRITISH MOVIES OF 2012

Q1.	Margaret Thatcher	Q11.	Contraband
Q2.	Skyfall	Q12.	Coriolanus
Q3.	The Best Exotic Marigold Hotel	Q13.	War Horse
Q4.	Colin Firth	Q14.	The Girl with the Dragon Tattoo
Q5.	Sir Ian McKellen	Q15.	The Dark Knight Rises
Q6.	Les Miserables	Q16.	Looper
Q7.	The Sweeney	Q17.	Rise of the Guardians
Q8.	Daniel Radcliffe	Q18.	Seeking a Friend for the End of the World
Q9.	Wrath of the Titans	Q19.	Crispian Mills
Q10.	The Wee Man	Q20.	The Grind

PART 4: GREAT BRITISH SIGHTS

Q1.	Tower of London		Q11.	O2 Arena
Q2.	St Paul's Cathedral		Q12.	Stonehenge
Q3.	Royal Botanical Gardens, Kew		Q13.	Royal Pavilion, Brighton
Q4.	Eden Project		Q14.	Lake District
Q5.	York Minster		Q15.	LEGOLAND
Q6.	Blackpool Tower		Q16.	Madame Tussauds
Q7.	Tate Modern		Q17.	Hampton Court Palace
Q8.	Alton Towers		Q18.	Chartwell
Q9.	Edinburgh Castle		Q19.	Battle Abbey (built on the site of the Battle of Hastings)
Q10.	Giant's Causeway		Q20.	Wallace Monument

PART 5: GREAT BRITISH SOAPS

EASTENDERS

Q1.	Heather Trott
Q2.	Letitia Dean (aka Sharon Watts/Mitchell/Rickman)
Q3.	Ian Beale
Q4.	Roxy
Q5.	Janine
Q6.	On the roof
Q7.	Phil
Q8.	Susan Tully
Q9.	Walford
Q10.	Nick Berry

CORONATION STREET

Q1.	Terry Duckworth
Q2.	Dennis Tanner
Q3.	Paul Kershaw
Q4.	Rob Donovan
Q5.	A laptop
Q6.	Smoke alarms, so that he could sell them (turned out they were faulty!)
Q7.	Ruby
Q8.	Fare Ladies
Q9.	£12,000
Q10.	Izzy and Katy

BEST OF THE REST

Q1.	Chester
Q2.	A flash forward episode
Q3.	Amy Barnes
Q4.	Home and Away
Q5.	Eldorado
Q6.	Crossroads
Q7.	Casualty
Q8.	Holby City
Q9.	1972
Q10.	1989